Rainbows, Halos, and Other Wonders

Rainbows, Halos, and Other Wonders

LIGHT AND COLOR IN THE ATMOSPHERE

Kenneth Heuer

FELLOW OF THE ROYAL ASTRONOMICAL SOCIETY

Illustrated with photographs and prints

DODD,
MEAD
&
COMPANY
New York

FRONTISPIECE. *Glory observed from a balloon.* On February 16, 1873, Gaston Tissandier, the French aeronaut, saw concentric circles of various colors around the image of the basket (Chapter 16).

ENDPAPER. *Snowflakes.* Luminous rings seen around the sun and moon are formed by the refraction of light through ice crystals such as these and ice needles which constitute cirrus and cirrostratus clouds (Chapter 13). This remarkable photomicrograph was taken by W. A. Bentley.

Printed in the United States of America

1 2 3 4 5 6 7 8 9 10

Library of Congress Cataloging in Publication Data

Heuer, Kenneth.
Rainbows, halos, and other wonders.

Bibliography: p.
Includes index.
SUMMARY: Describes the phenomena occurring when light interacts with the earth's atmosphere causing rainbows, mirages, coronas, twinkling stars, and numerous other beautiful and seemingly mysterious optical effects.
1. Meteorological optics—Juvenile literature.
[1. Meteorological optics] I. Title.
QC975.2.H48 551.5'6 77-16865
ISBN 0-396-07557-6

To Two Friends,

Richard and Brownie

The shudder of awe is humanity's highest faculty,
Even though this world is forever altering its values. . . .

Goethe, *Faust*, Part II

Contents

Illustrations

Rainbows, Halos, and Other Wonders

Preface

The atmosphere is filled with many wonderful displays of light and color. They are among the most awe-inspiring and unearthly spectacles in nature. Some of them are so strange that people have thought these features were tricks of their own imagination.

There are the beautiful colors of the twilight sky, red where the sun went down, through orange, yellow, and green to blue, and even purple in the distance. There are the superglories of the heavens—the rainbow, the halo, and the corona. There are the things in the sky we misjudge, owing to the deception of perspective—the full moon, immense on the horizon, growing smaller and smaller as it approaches the point overhead. Because of the curved path of light through the air, there are the things we see where they are not within sight, such as the sun above the horizon when it has just set below. And there are even things we see that are not there to see—mirages!

Light from the sun, moon, and stars, and other sources passes through the earth's atmosphere and is changed in various ways

Inferior mirage, Death Valley, California. A lake appears in the distance—but the lake is actually not there (Chapter 7).

to produce these effects. The study of them is known as *atmospheric*, or *meteorological, optics.* Meteorology is the science dealing with the atmosphere and its phenomena, and optics is the science dealing with light.

Some of the effects are common; they are part of everyday life. Others can be seen frequently if you know what to look for, though they may be unfamiliar to you as yet. Or you may have seen them and wondered what they were. Still others are rare. Indeed, some of these effects occur only occasionally in a lifetime; the most experienced observer may wait year after year to see them.

There is a saying, "Chance favors the prepared mind." In terms of optical phenomena, this simply means that if a phenomenon occurs and you know what to look for, you will have a greater chance of seeing it. Moreover, you will find it more fascinating because of your ability to look at it from a scientific point of view. This book on atmospheric optics, then, should help you to see and appreciate the wonders of light and color in the open air.

The features of the atmosphere are arranged here, for the most part, according to the physical processes causing them, and there are personal accounts of a number of the phenomena I have observed.

The book is illustrated with photographs and prints. A photograph has the virtue of showing the actual effect. But a picture etched into a metal plate or cut into a wooden block often shows an optical phenomenon more clearly than the chemical action of light upon a film in a camera. Some of the best pictures of these effects were made in the nineteenth century and are included in these pages.

For anyone who has ever wondered why the stars twinkle, or if you can walk under the arch of a rainbow, or why the sky is blue, this book has been written.

1

Seeing the Sun When It Is Not There

The fact that the sun may be seen where it is not in view is seemingly contradictory. Yet it is undeniably true. This curious effect is caused by *refraction*.

Refraction is the process in which rays of light are bent from their original straight-line course in passing from one medium to another of different density. Rays of light traveling perpendicularly, at right angles, to the surface separating the two media are never refracted, however.

You may have seen how a pencil or a stick partly submerged in water appears to bend sharply at the waterline and take up a distorted shape. This is a common example of refraction. The bending is due to the fact that the light rays travel at different speeds in media of different densities, in this case air and water.

Refraction can also take place within a single medium. The air varies a great deal in density, and light is bent on passing through it. The density difference is due to differences of temperature and humidity within separate air layers. It is also due to a steady increase in density of the air from its outer reaches to

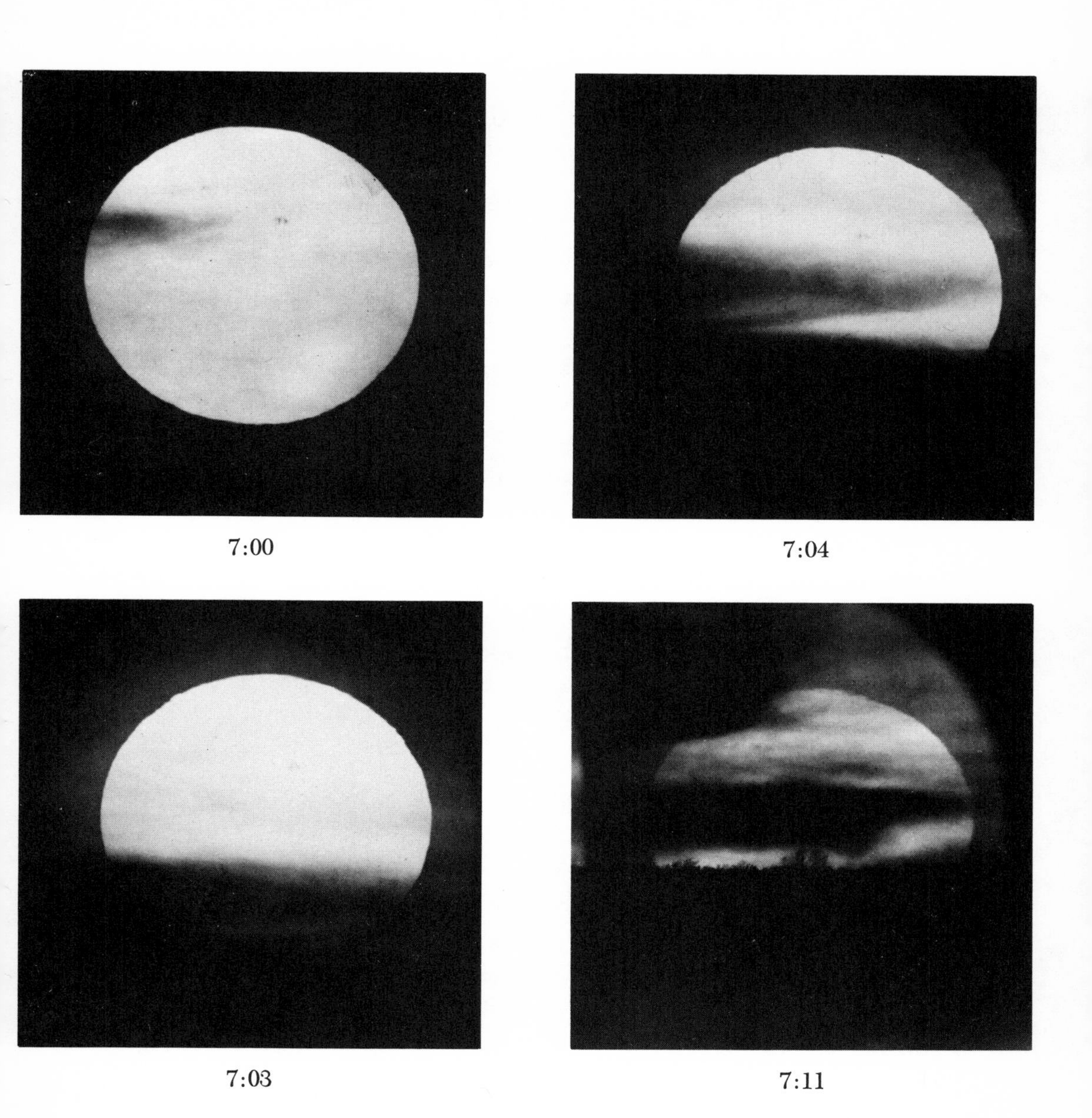

Oval sun near the horizon. The sun is flattened by refraction as it sets.

the surface of the earth. Because of this last condition, when the sun, moon, and stars are close to the horizon, light coming from them is bent into a curved path. Whether rising or setting, this makes these celestial objects visible when they are really about a half degree below the horizon, an amount approximately equal to the apparent diameter of the sun and of the moon. So the entire solar or lunar disc may be seen above the horizon when it is actually below.

The refraction increases very rapidly near the horizon, for the amount of air the light ray must travel across increases. As the sun, say, or the moon, approaches the horizon, the light from its lower edge is bent more than that from its upper edge. Consequently, its lower edge appears proportionately more elevated than its upper edge, and this makes the sun appear flattened on the horizon. The flattening amounts to about one-fifth of the sun's diameter. You may have wondered about its misshapen condition, for this is a familiar sight, especially when the sun sets over a body of water.

2
Green and Blue Flashes

"To the naked eye its appearance has generally been that of a green spark of large size and great intensity, very similar to one of the effects seen when the sun shines upon a well-cut diamond."

This vivid description of the *green flash* was made by D. Winstanley in the last century. During a period of eighteen months, he observed the phenomenon "certainly more than fifty times" from his residence in Blackpool, England, on the Irish Sea. As the upper edge of the sun disappeared in a clear sky below a distant horizon, its final starlike point and the surrounding sky occasionally flashed out in a deep brilliant green.

In order to understand the green flash, we should remember that white light is composed of light of many colors. When white light is passed through a glass prism, the components of the light are refracted differently. Each color is bent to a different degree in accordance with its particular wavelength. The result is a rainbow band of colors called the *spectrum*, consisting of red, orange, yellow, green, blue, indigo, and violet regions which grade into each other. The process in which white light is broken up into its different colors is called *dispersion*. It is important to note that the wavelength of blue light is about half that of red, and the blue-violet end of the spectrum is refracted more than the red.

The large refraction for celestial objects near the horizon is connected with a relatively large prismatic dispersion. By virtue of this, when the upper edge of the sun sinks below the horizon, the component colors of its white light must disappear in the order of their capability of being refracted. The red, being bent the least by the refraction due to the earth's atmosphere, disappears first. The last to go is the violet part of the spectrum. By the time the red, orange, and yellow have disappeared, the color is distinctly green. This results in the appearance of the green flash.

The flash can take other forms. If the atmosphere is both abnormally refractive and abnormally clear, a fully developed blue coloration can be seen—the *blue flash*. In rare cases, a continuous spectral color change from yellow to violet has been reported. The flash is seen also just as the sun's edge appears above the horizon at sunrise. Here, too, it may be blue as well as

Sunset with green flash. The development of a green flash is seen in these black-and-white reproductions of color photographs taken with a camera having a telescopic lens. At top, the sun has nearly set, and the upper rim of the segment is green. In the next two photographs, a green flash is separating from the sun's disc. At bottom, the sun has set, and a green flash remains hanging above the horizon. The time between the top and bottom views was 8.4 seconds, and the flash vanished after about 1 second as pure emerald green. The pictures, which have been enlarged, were taken on December 28, 1955, by C. Treusch, S.J., in collaboration with D. J. K. O'Connell.

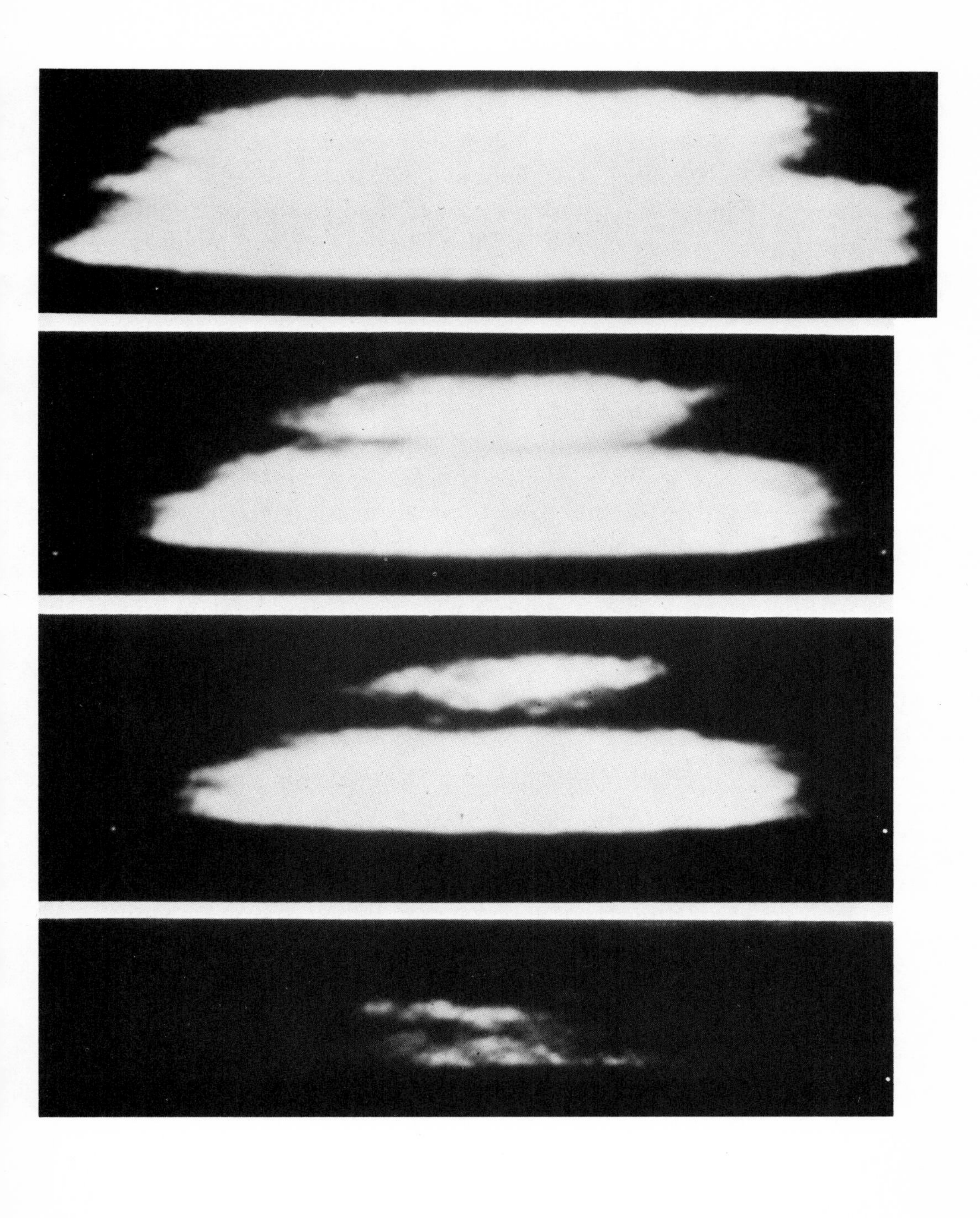

green. If it changes color, it does so in the reverse order.

One of the best places to observe the green flash is over the sea, where the conditions of a distant horizon and a clear sky are fulfilled. It was, therefore, natural for a number of people to imagine that the green flash was due to sunlight shining through the crests of waves on the far-off horizon, or even through the curved water surface of the ocean. The many observations of the green flash over a land horizon are a sufficient argument against the sea wave theory, however.

A more plausible explanation, which still has supporters, attributes the effect to retinal fatigue. It is a well-known fact that after looking into a bright light, our eyes become strained. When we look away from the light, we see the complementary color. According to this theory, our eyes are overpowered in looking at the red sunset and we see, immediately afterward, the complement of red, which is green. The explanation is obviously wrong, for it cannot account for the flash seen at sunrise, before the solar disk appears in the heavens.

The green flash lasts only a few seconds under the most favorable conditions. But during Admiral Richard E. Byrd's expedition to Little America (78° south) in 1929, the phenomenon was observed for 35 minutes! The sun, rising for the first time at the end of the long polar night, was moving exactly along the horizon when this occurred. In another remarkable observation made by C. Mostyn and A. A. Nijland, the green flash appeared three times at one sunset. Big waves conveniently heaved up the observers' ship, "causing as it were two sunsets with a sunrise between them."

The phenomenon has also been seen on rare occasions in connection with the moon and the brightest planets, Venus and Jupiter.

3
Twinkling of Stars

Almost everyone has seen the *twinkling* or, as it is called by scientists, the *scintillation*, of the stars. On a cold winter night, when you look at a bright star near the eastern or western horizon, twinkling is especially noticeable. The star rapidly changes in brightness and often in color, adding much to the beauty of the sky. If you are fortunate enough to look through a telescope, you see another effect—the star changes position, or dances. As seen through a large telescope, the star's position is as unsteady as a moth about a flame.

This flickering is not something taking place in the star itself. The fact that it is more conspicuous as the star gets closer to the horizon is evidence that the atmosphere is the cause of the twinkling, for near the horizon the star's light comes through a greater thickness of air.

The seeming changes in brightness of a twinkling star are due to the movement of masses of air of different densities across the line of sight. This causes a star's light, which appears to come from a mere point, to be bent in different directions. At one

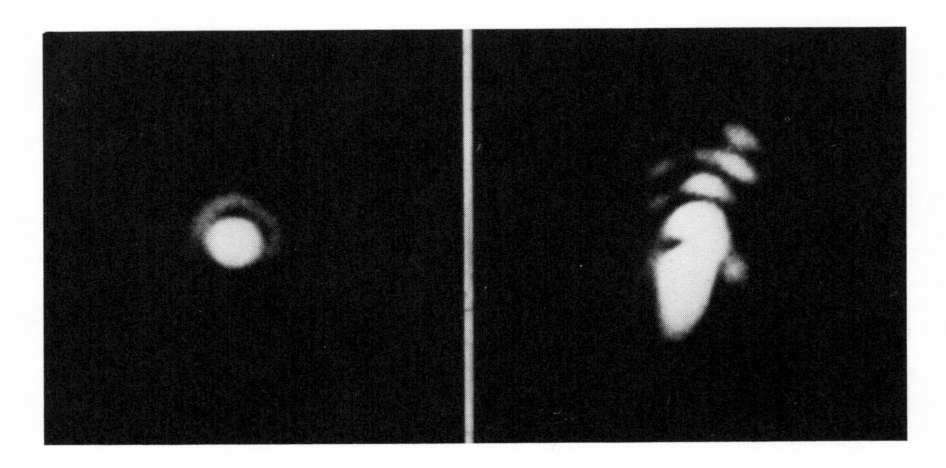

Capturing star's twinkle. Scintillation is a difficult effect to capture in a still photograph. Here it is illustrated by using a laser beam to imitate the star image. At left is the undistorted image. The other photograph shows the image through waviness caused by rising heat.

instant very few rays reach the eye and at another many. If a bright star close to the horizon not only changes in brightness but also in color, the refraction of the star's light is so great as to spread the light out into its several colors. Each color follows its own path, so much out of a straight line and so different from the others that first one color and then another comes to the eye in both rapid and irregular succession. Sirius, the Dog Star, in the constellation Canis Major, the Larger Dog, is remarkable in this respect because of its great brilliancy. Visible in the winter months rather low in the sky, it flashes rainbow colors.

In the same general way, inequalities in the atmosphere produce rapid changes in the apparent position of a star as seen in a telescope.

The size of the air masses producing scintillation is rather small, of the order of a few centimeters to a few decimeters. A centimeter is a measure of length equal to one hundredth of a meter, or about two-fifths of an inch, and a decimeter is equivalent to one-tenth of a meter.

4

Scintillation of Planets

Aristotle, the Greek thinker who lived over two thousand years ago, noted that the stars twinkle while the planets shine with more or less steady light. This is true: planets scintillate far less than stars. It seems odd, because in other respects the planets and stars appear quite alike to the naked eye.

The cause of this difference is easily explained. The stars are huge globes of gas like the sun. But because they are at such great distances from the earth, they appear as mere points of light even in the largest telescopes. On the other hand, the planets, which are not as far away as the stars, are seen as luminous discs through the telescope. Each point of the disc twinkles like a star. However, this twinkling of the different points does not take place at the same time, for the rays from different points take slightly different paths through the atmosphere and do not encounter the same irregularities. Therefore, the general sum of light does not vary, and the planet's light is quite steady.

When the planets are close to the horizon, and the disturbance in the air is very pronounced, however, the scintillation is noticeable. The planets change in brightness and color, especially Mercury, which is the smallest planet and consequently has a very small disc. Even the rims of the sun and moon scintillate under favorable conditions.

Jupiter. The photograph, taken with a reflecting telescope, shows the luminous disc of the largest planet.

5
Terrestrial Scintillation

Bright lights on the earth a few miles from the observer scintillate at night quite as clearly as do the stars in the sky and for essentially the same reason. Due to the constant rising of warm air masses and falling of cold and conflicting winds, the light reaching the eye is inconstant. As one draws nearer to these lights, the twinkling becomes less and finally disappears.

I have often noticed rows of twinkling streetlamps along the distant avenues of seaside towns. They are a splendid sight, viewed from a ship entering port. And city lights seen at night from an airplane present another fine display of *terrestrial scintillation*. When one looks down through the turbulent atmosphere on a flight across the country, the bright lights of the cities below glitter like jewels. Terrestrial scintillation is the

Aerial view of Manhattan. Against a spectacular background of clouds, night falls over New York and, due to atmospheric turbulence, the city lights sparkle like diamonds. Although difficult to capture in a still photograph, the scintillation would be quite dramatic if one were to make a moving picture of the lights. Taken on January 9, 1959.

general term for scintillation phenomena observed in light from sources lying within the earth's atmosphere, while *astronomical scintillation* is observed in light from sources beyond the limits of the earth such as stars.

Shimmer is a type of terrestrial scintillation. Nearly everyone has observed objects across a heated, dry surface that appear to dance or shimmer. On a quiet, cloudless, summer day, this phenomenon is seen over a roadway or field of stubble. Or if you have ever looked above a stove used to melt asphalt for the surface of a street, you will have noticed that the objects in the distance seem to quiver so much as to be greatly distorted. The air itself seems to be no longer transparent. Everything shimmers above a hot tin roof, and a stretch of sand heated by the sun brings about the same effect.

Shimmer is another example of irregular refraction and is due to the upward and downward movement of air masses of different density that always occurs over such a surface. The effect is also know as *laurence*, in memory of St. Laurence, a third-century Christian martyr who was burned alive on a gridiron!

Optical haze is caused in the same way. Haze is a lack of transparency in the air, commonly due to dust, but sometimes due to the unequal refraction of light passing through air of varying density. Thus, on warm days, when the atmosphere is relatively free from dust, the outlines of distant objects often seem vague and indistinct. A definite white haze obstructs the vision. Coastlines are often shrouded in it. As a result of marked temperature inequalities common along land bordering the sea, they are invisible from a short distance offshore. This lack of transparency in the air is a pleasing phenomenon.

6

Looming, Towering, Sinking, and Stooping

In some cases, instead of decreasing with height above the earth, the temperature of the air increases. This condition is known as a *temperature inversion*. On calm, clear nights, as the earth cools rapidly by radiation, the air near the surface is cooled both by radiation and by contact with the cold earth. In this way, it often becomes colder and denser than the air higher up.

When a marked increase in the density of the air exists near the surface, a phenomenon known as *looming* may occur. Objects normally below the horizon come into sight. A ship, for example, which is actually below the horizon, appears above it. The effect is seen frequently in high northern latitudes or arctic waters.

In this optical phenomenon, the altitude of objects on the earth is increased in much the same way as that of celestial objects, such as the sun being made visible when it is actually below the horizon. Refraction causes a change in the apparent altitude of all objects on the earth, due to passage of light obliquely through air strata of varying density. The more rap-

Telescopic appearance of ships in the arctic. Towering and stooping are portrayed in this picture of phenomena seen by William Scoresby, Jr., while navigating in the icy sea near West Greenland on June 28, 1820. In the picture, one ship (e) is strangely distorted, its masts appearing at least twice their proper height, while the masts of two ships (f and g) seem to be scarcely one-half of their proper altitude. The appearance of

d e f g

the ships and ice with their inverted images in the air (b, c, and d) is explained in Chapter 7. A large ridge of ice on the horizon (a) is raised into the air in the form of an obelisk, or upright pillar. The remarkable phenomena were seen by the Engish arctic explorer about the same time, but they occupied a much larger space than shown.

idly the density of the air decreases with increase of height, the more pronounced is the down-bending of a ray of light which passes close to the surface and the farther one can see over the rim of the earth. Consequently, in the early morning after a calm, clear night, the time and circumstance of a strong temperature inversion, objects loom up.

The condition of the atmosphere that produces looming often gives rise to another phenomenon, *towering*. This is the apparent vertical stretching of objects some distance away to unusual heights. The more rapid the downward curvature of the ray paths at the observer, the more elevated will objects seem to be. Such curvature may be very large. If at this moment the inversion layer is situated in such a way that the rays of light to the observer from the top of an object are more curved than those from the bottom, the object will appear not only elevated but also vertically magnified. It will tower and, consequently, seem to draw nearer.

I recall seeing this effect for the first time as an impressionable child. The object was a nearby hill on which a house was situated and to which I was returning. In my absence, I found the hill had mysteriously become a mountain and its trees giants. The effect is extremely eerie. You will find it so, too, even though you know how it is produced.

Because of looming, lights beyond the horizon are often visible to the sailor. When the real light is seen, the effect of towering may stretch it upward. Hulls, smokestacks, and masts of ships are affected in the same way.

From the explanation of looming and towering, it should be clear that if the density of the air should increase less rapidly than it does as a rule with approach to the earth's surface, then a ray would bend down less than it usually does. This would cause objects normally just above the horizon to disappear below it. Called *sinking*, the phenomenon is exactly the opposite of looming and is also most often observed at sea.

At times, distant objects seem to be foreshortened vertically. This apparent decrease in height is called *stooping*. It is a special case of sinking in which the curvature of light rays due to atmospheric refraction decreases with elevation. Stooping produces effects just as strange as those due to towering.

7
Superior and Inferior Mirages

Looming and towering are forms of *mirage.* A mirage is an optical effect in which an image of some object is made to appear displaced from its true postion. It is due to the refraction of light as it passes through layers of the atmosphere that are not alike.

A *superior mirage* is very striking. If it occurs at sea, the image of a distant ship may appear floating upside down in the sky, with a second upright image of the ship above that! Because one or more images of an actual object are observed directly above it, the name "superior" is given to this type of mirage. The image nearest the object is always seen inverted. It appears as if reflected from an overhead flat mirror.

For an object to appear above its surface position, there must be a strong temperature inversion some distance above the earth's surface. The eye of the observer must be below the lighter warm air, in the cold zone. In passing through the cold layer of air and warm air above it, light rays from the ship are bent downward to the observer's eye. As in the case of looming,

Superior mirage at sea

this kind of mirage is seen over cold land or water.

Because of the almost ghostly appearance and disappearance of entire ships due to this bending of light, the legend of the Flying Dutchman is kept alive. In the legend, a Dutch mariner is condemned for his crimes to sail the seas till the day of judgment. When superstitious sailors see such a mirage, they think it is the mariner's spectral ship, which is believed to be a bad omen.

Another striking apparition is viewed in ice fields in high northern latitudes. There the inverted forms of distant icebergs seem suspended in the sky.

The *inferior mirage* is probably the most common form of the phenomenon. When you are out riding in the family car, you may have noticed that a paved road heated by the rays of the sun

Superior mirage on land

appears to be wet a few hundred feet ahead of you. It is remarkable how these pools of water are not disturbed by the traffic, while leaves, paper, and dust are whirled about by the flow of automobiles along the highway. And you may have seen people unconsciously "splashing" along or across the flooded highway. Actually, you are badly deceived. What you see is not a water surface but an image of the sky, a mirage.

In this type of mirage, the air next to the earth becomes much warmer than the air immediately above. The eye of the observer must be somewhat above the heated layer, in the cooler, denser overlying air. Light rays from the sky in passing through these layers are refracted upward to the observer's eye. Because of the bending of the light rays, the observer sees the image of the distant sky turned upside down. The inferior mirage gets its name from the fact that it always appears *below* the actual object, inverted in position. Therefore, the image seems to be reflected from a flat mirror underfoot.

When observed from a slight elevation, the warm surface of a sandy valley in a desert region takes on the appearance of a lake. This is the same illusion as the road mirage seen on a large scale. In addition to the inversion of the low blue sky giving the appearance of a water surface, the inverted images of distant trees, buildings, or other objects are often seen. The whole effect produced may look like a quiet body of water only a mile or so away, with objects on the far-off shore reflected and shimmering

Inferior mirage in the desert

in it. But it is a curious body of water. It flows back as far and as fast as the observer may approach it, flows toward him if he should retreat from it, and completely hides everything below its apparent surface. It is no wonder that desert travelers are frequently lead astray by this phenomenon.

8

Lateral Mirage and Fata Morgana

Occasionally, mirages are seen along walls and cliffs whose temperatures differ markedly from the air a few yards from them. These *lateral mirages* are produced by vertical sheets of unusually dense or unusually rare atmosphere and are in every way like those due to similar horizontal layers.

You can see a lateral mirage quite easily. Find an even wall at least ten yards long that faces south and on which the sun is shining. Rest your head against the wall and look along it sideways while a friend, as far off along the wall as possible, holds a bright object closer and closer to it. An ordinary house key, shining in the sun, might be used. As soon as the key is within a few inches of the wall, it becomes distorted, and its image appears to approach the key from the wall's surface. At times, an image of the whole hand holding the key is made to appear displaced from its true position. This mirage has the same explanation as the common road mirage.

In addition to the three types of simple mirages already described, there are some very remarkable complex mirages pro-

Lateral mirage of boy along a sunlit wall. At a distance of 180 yards from the observer, one can see the image of the boy and the beginning of a second image (left background). The temperature of the wall was 4.5° C. higher than that of the air.

duced by complex temperature distributions. The famous *Fata Morgana* that occurs over the Strait of Messina between Italy and Sicily is an example of this type.

Under favorable conditions, objects such as cliffs and cottages are transformed into fantastic castles and towers that, alike, rise into the sky and sink beneath the sea. This mirage received its name from Fata Morgana, Morgan the fairy, who Italian poets imagined as dwelling in a crystal palace beneath the water. The conversion of cliffs and cottages into marvelous palaces was a demonstration of her powers.

The name Fata Morgana is now given to all such complicated mirages, wherever they occur in the world, as at Toyama Bay, an inlet of the Sea of Japan. The mirages combine the effects of inferior and superior mirages and are produced by a cold layer of air sandwiched between two layers of hot air. This is an unstable condition subject to quick changes. In addition to producing a double mirage which changes rapidly in form, the cold, middle layer acts also as a kind of cylindrical lens that magnifies vertically distant objects seen through it. No wonder we see castles in the air!

Fata Morgana. The complicated mirage is depicted as it occurs during a morning in very calm weather over the Strait of Messina.

9
Unidentified Flying Objects

Mirages have also appeared as *unidentified flying objects* (UFOs), and many people have been misled by them. The term "unidentified flying object" has come to mean any object or optical phenomenon, usually aerial, that the observer cannot readily explain. In the popular mind, UFO suggests visitors from outer space. It is very probable that other planetary systems exist, and a large section of the population has taken the view that superior extraterrestrial civilizations might visit the earth from time to time. According to some people, the visits became more numerous when mankind released nuclear energy, thereby increasing extraterrestrial concern. However, it has been shown that most of the UFO reports are caused by aircraft, balloons, birds, bright planets, meteors, twinkling stars, auroras—some hoaxes and outright hallucinations—and mirages.

In one case, where there was a warm air layer over cold, it is probable that the observer saw the running lights of a ship below the normal horizon, but made visible as the result of mirage. In another, a fighter pilot on a practice training mission

Superior mirage observed in a balloon. In his balloon ascension of August 16, 1868, above Calais, the French seaport on the Strait of Dover, Gaston Tissandier saw the image of a steamer and several small boats sailing upside down on an inverted ocean. The image of the sea, with the greenish shade of the water and the light effects of the shore, appeared in the sky above. Similar mirages may have revealed themselves to modern observers as unidentified flying objects.

over Detroit, Michigan, tried to intercept "a ragged formation of aircraft." It is likely that these objects were actually an inferior mirage, for they appeared slightly below the level of the aircraft. A layer of heated air, trapped temporarily below a cooler layer, could cause the pilot to see the image of the sky in a few spots. This phenomenon is quite similar to the familiar road mirage.

Actual "dog fights" between a confused military pilot and a star or planet on the horizon have been recorded. Sometimes a layer of warm air, enclosed between two layers of cold air, can act as a lens, throwing forward a pulsing, spinning, colored, saucer-like image of a planet. Thinking they were dealing with a nearby flying object, pilots have frequently tried to stop the progress of the image, which evades all attempts to cut if off. The distance may appear to change as the planet fades or increases in brightness. This phenomenon of star mirage is both realistic and frightening.

Although most UFO sightings have been explained in a common-sense way, a number of scientists have concluded that a small percentage of the most reliable UFO reports give definite indications of the presence of extraterrestrial visitors!

10
Rainbows

Like other spectacular events in the heavens, many people believe the rainbow is an omen. An imminent supernatural occurrence seems to lie beyond this spectacle. Pliny, the Roman naturalist and author who lived in the first century after the birth of Christ, said the rainbow foretold a heavy winter or a war. To the Iranian Moslems, even the brilliance of the colors of the rainbow has significance. A prominent red means war, green means abundance, and yellow brings death. The Arawak of South America recognize the rainbow as a fortunate sign if it is seen over the sea. When it appears on land, however, these Indians believe it is an evil spirit looking for a victim.

In the mythologies of several peoples, the rainbow is a bridge between heaven and earth. The North American Catawba Indians of the Southeast and the Tlingit of the Northwest both regard it as the road of the dead. In Siberia, the rainbow is the bow of the thunder god. Among a group of tribes of northeastern Siberia, it is the tongue of the sun. And the Samoyeds, a Siberian Mongolian people, call it *munbano*, the hem of the sun god's coat.

Noah's Sacrifice. After the Flood, Noah left the ark and built an altar to the Lord and offered burnt offerings on it. Then God set the rainbow in the clouds as a sign of the covenant between Him and Noah and every living creature—the promise that the waters should never again become a flood to destroy the earth. Painted by P. J. de Loutherbourg.

One of the most beautiful sights in nature, the rainbow has become in our culture a symbol of renewed hope or, in the words of Genesis, a "covenant between God and every living creature." This familiar feature of the atmosphere appears during or immediately following local showers, when the sun is shining and the air contains raindrops. The bow is divided into bands displaying the different colors of the spectrum and is formed by the refraction and *reflection* of the sun's rays in drops of rain. Reflection is simply the return of light waves from surfaces.

When a ray of sunlight enters a drop of water, a part of it does not pass directly through but is reflected from the inner surface and emerges from the side from which it entered. Moreover, it is refracted both on entering and leaving the water drop. This process, repeated in the same manner for an immense number of drops, produces the *primary rainbow*, which appears in front of the observer, who has his back to the sun. It has the red band on the outer edge and the blue-to-violet on the inner edge.

Another larger bow is often seen outside the primary rainbow and parallel to it. This *secondary rainbow* is produced in a similar way, but the sun's light is reflected twice before emerging from the raindrop. For this reason, the color sequence is reversed; red is on the inside edge. And because there is a loss of light with each reflection, it is not as bright as the primary rainbow. The region between the two bows is comparatively dark, for it lacks entirely both the once- and the twice-reflected rays.

The *tertiary rainbow* has about the same size as the primary rainbow and colors in the same order. It results from three internal light reflections and lies between the observer and the sun. That is, the observer would have to look through a rain curtain toward the sun in order to see this rainbow. It is so faint that it is seen rarely in nature. In fact, there is no reliable evidence that it has *ever* been seen, though a tertiary bow is theoretically possible.

Narrow bands of color, essentially red or red and green, appear now and then, along the inner side of the primary rainbow and along the outer side of the secondary rainbow. Such bands are called *supernumerary rainbows* and are frequently so faint as to be visible only to an experienced observer.

Each of these rainbows is part of a circle whose center is on the line connecting the observer's eyes with the sun. At sunrise or sunset, when the sun is on the horizon, it is possible to see a complete semicircle on the opposite horizon. We cannot follow the rainbow further than the horizon because we cannot see raindrops floating below it. However, completely circular rainbows are visible from aircraft at a certain height above the earth.

Although the lengths of the different orders of rainbows vary a great deal, both with the parts of the complete circles that are visible and with their distance from the observer, their angular radii are always essentially the same. For example, the primary rainbow always has a radius of about 42°. To understand what is meant by this, imagine a line drawn from the eye to the center of the rainbow and another line going to any point on the red part of the circular arc. These two lines would make an angle of 42° at the eye of the observer and go to the end points of the rainbow's radius. A radius, as you know, is a straight line joining the center of a circle and a point on its circumference, and a degree is the unit of measurement of plane angles. In each kind of rainbow, the angular distance from the center of the bow to any given one of the colors is always the same, 42° to the red of the primary bow and 50° to the red of the secondary.

There are many theories of rainbows but not enough observational data. Such material is needed to apply to the theoretical findings. In this connection, an unsolved problem of the rainbow may be mentioned: the fluctuations of colors during lightning and thunder. This striking observation needs to be verified objectively and explained.

11

Popular Questions About the Rainbow

Many people ask questions about the rainbow. One question frequently asked is, How far away is the rainbow? At best this question can be answered by saying that its distance from the observer is exactly that of the raindrops that produce it. Its distance, then, extends from the nearest to the farthest drops that contribute any part of the colored light. The closest of these raindrops may be miles away. Or they may be only a few feet away. On one occasion, an observer saw a rainbow between himself and a wood three yards from him. The raindrops themselves were therefore still nearer. In the case of a spray from a lawn sprinkler in which a rainbow appears, you can reach right out into the bow and even grasp the "pot of gold."

The idea that a pot of gold is to be found at the rainbow's end is an old superstition. In Silesia, a region in Eastern Europe, it is said that the angels put the gold there and that only a nude man can obtain the prize. In the Balkan state of Romania it is believed that the rainbow stands with each end in a river. Anyone creeping to its end on hands and knees and drinking the water

Several rainbows at one time. The primary rainbow is seen with supernumeraries along its inner side. Some distance outside is the larger secondary rainbow.

the rainbow touches will instantly change sex.

Can you go under a rainbow's arch and come out on the other side? This is impossible, although there is a European superstition that anyone passing beneath the rainbow will be transformed, man into woman, woman into man. The rainbow is always in front of the observer, who has his back to the sun. It cannot have any other position, except for the tertiary rainbow, which is of too low an intensity to be visible.

Why are rainbows most often seen in the summer? The answer is simple. The formation of the rainbow requires the existence at the same time of rain and sunshine, a condition that occurs far more frequently in the summer than in the winter. If you ever hear anyone say he has seen a rainbow in the falling snow, you can be sure that the snow was half melted.

Why are rainbows rarely seen at noon? You will recall that the center of the rainbow is exactly opposite the sun. Therefore, the higher the sun ascends, the more the center of the rainbow, and therefore the whole rainbow, descends. More and more of the circumference disappears below the horizon until the uppermost tip of the primary rainbow just grazes the horizon when the altitude of the sun is 42°, the radius of the bow. During the summer, the rainbow season, the elevation of the sun in our part of the world is greater than 42°, or even 50°, the radius of the secondary rainbow. This is why a rainbow at noon is an impossible summer phenomenon, except in high latitudes, where the sun is lower in the sky.

Do two people ever see the same rainbow? The answer is, "no." As the eyes of people do not occupy the same place in space, each observer sees a different rainbow, that is, a bow made by different drops of water.

Since raindrops are constantly in motion, why does the rainbow always have the same appearance? As it falls within the limits of the rays that produce the phenomenon, each raindrop contributes only for a moment to it. Yet its place is filled up so rapidly by the succeeding raindrops that the effect is the same.

12

Moonbows, Fogbows, and Dew Bows

Rainbows are as unlike each other as trees in a forest. The *moonbow* is well known, but it is rarely seen, except along certain coasts abounding with frequent showers and above great waterfalls. A lunar rainbow is formed in the same optical manner as the ordinary rainbow, but the light comes from the moon instead of the sun. The bow is naturally faint and can be seen practically only when the moon is full. Colors are usually very difficult to detect in it.

There are great contrasts in the brightness and purity of the colors of rainbows. The rainbow of the departing thunderstorm is sharply defined and brilliant, while the bow that sometimes appears in a fog or mist is ill-defined and slightly colored. This is known as a *fogbow* or *white rainbow*.

Rather large drops of water of nearly the same size produce the brightest bows and the purest colors. When the drops are very small, as in the case of fog, the bow has the appearance of a white band with faintly tinted borders. It generally has a radius between 37° and 40°.

A fogbow frequently appears when the bright beam of a searchlight behind us penetrates the mist in front of us. And against a dark background, streetlamps often give rise to feeble fogbows when minute water droplets are suspended in the atmosphere.

A *red rainbow*, which is sometimes amazingly bright, can be observed, too. During the last five or ten minutes before sunset all the colors of the rainbow are seen to fade, except the red. Finally, only an all-red arc is left and remains visible even for a few minutes after the sun has set. The lower part of the arc is screened off by that time, so it appears to begin at some height above the horizon. Here we are being shown the spectrum of the sunlight and how its composition changes during sunset. This change is caused by the scattering of the shorter wavelengths, a process explained in a later chapter.

A *reflection rainbow* is formed by light rays which have been reflected from a smooth surface of water. The center of this rainbow is at the same distance of the sun above the horizon but in the opposite part of the heavens. When it is visible, an ordinary rainbow frequently will be seen on the same sheet of rain. Then the two rainbows cut into one another at the horizon. When a small wave disturbs the reflecting water surface, the shape of the reflection bow may change into vertical shafts. The primary reflection bow is usually seen; others are likely to be too faint to be visible. This rainbow is not to be confused with a *reflected rainbow*, whose image is seen occasionally in large pools. A reflected rainbow appears upside down, and the arc of the bow is less than the bow seen in a direct manner and, therefore, is likely to look flatter.

I have seen a *horizontal rainbow* from time to time on the grass of a well-cut lawn and on other surfaces. It is formed by

Incomplete reflection rainbow with ordinary bow. On September 11, 1874, at 5:40 P.M., this unusual phenomenon was observed in Saint Andrews, a seaport in East Scotland. Sketched by T. Hodge.

dewdrops and is also called a *dew bow*. In the morning, when the dewdrops on the grass are lit by sunbeams, the bow stands out on the ground in the shape of a curve known as a *hyperbola*, not as a circle. In the course of the day, with a change in the height of the sun, the bow would become an *ellipse*, though this curve of light has not been seen often. The phenomenon is both beautiful and fascinating. The grass seems to be filled with gleaming gems that change from one color to another as I shift my head.

The rainbow can also be seen on trees. Following an ice storm, trees in front of an observer whose back is to the sun glow in the several colors of the spectrum. The innumerable suspended drops on the tips of the tiny icicles and the casings of the twigs all have curved surfaces, which, like raindrops, refract and reflect the sun's rays and produce this lovely spectacle.

13

Halos in the Sky and on the Ground

A luminous ring around the sun or moon is a common occurrence. For hundreds of years, unenlightened people have believed these rings to be signs having all kinds of meanings. Even today some city inhabitants get excited when they see this phenomenon for the first time, and want to know if it foretells war or the world's end.

Solar or lunar *halos*, however, are simply the result of the refraction of light from the sun or moon by ice crystals in high, thin cirrus or cirrostratus clouds. As the cirrostratus clouds are the forerunners of storms, the worst a halo portends is that bad weather is approaching, and this is not certain. Henry Wadsworth Longfellow, the American poet, put the idea that halos have prognostic value into verse:

> For I fear a hurricane.
> Last night the moon had a golden ring
> And tonight no moon we see.

Incomplete solar halo

The most common halo is the *halo of 22°* radius. The ring is complete, except where the clouds producing it are not evenly distributed over the sky. A well-developed halo is red on the inside, followed by yellow and green, with blue on the outside. A *halo of 46°* is much more rarely seen. This appears fully twice as far from the sun or moon as the smaller halo. It has the same coloring but is not as bright.

The ice crystals through which the light passes are hexagonal plates or hexagonal columns. For the production of these halos, the six-sided prisms must be turned in all directions in the clouds. Then the refracted light forms a general circle of light around the sun or moon. The angles of refraction within the ice crystals determine the kind of halo that forms. Alternate hexagonal faces make an angle of 60° to each other, and the light that shines through this 60° prism is bent from its original direction by an angle that is equal to or greater than 22°. The sides and the ends of the hexagonal crystals make an angle of 90° to each other. This 90° prism can bend light from its original direction by an angle that is equal to or greater than 46°. In this way, it is possible to form 22° and 46° halos.

The 22° halo around the sun can be seen as many as a hun-

Halo seen in Norway. This unusual halo complex shows 22° and 46° halos, as well as other well-known phenomena of that kind (Chapter 14).

dred times a year, whereas the 46° halo can be observed only about once or twice a year. It seems odd, therefore, that many people have never noticed a solar halo. Several years ago a splendid 46° halo appeared in the sky when I was at the seashore. Everyone was busy sunning himself, and no one else seemed to notice the spectacle, although it was in plain sight of these modern sun worshippers. I wanted to tell the holiday makers what I saw, but I kept silent. My pleasure could not be shared.

The best way to observe a solar halo is to hold your hand in front of the sun to prevent yourself from being dazzled, or to stand in the shade of a house.

According to one report, an observer had the good fortune to see a halo around the setting sun and a halo around the rising full moon at the same time!

Halos are also seen on the ground, just as the rainbow is projected on a lawn as a dew bow. Both the 22° and 46° halos have been observed on a level snow surface as hyperbolas. Snow, of course, is composed of white or translucent ice crystals, chiefly in complex branched hexagonal form, which fall from the atmosphere. When the temperature is very low, look for *horizontal halos* about half an hour or an hour, at most, after sunrise or before sunset. Many years ago I saw these curves of light on freshly fallen snow, each with its apex toward me and consisting of a number of separate crystals twinkling with marvelous colors. When I moved, the streaks moved with me. What could the strange effect be? It was not till long after that I learned these were horizontal halos, though I suspect that this and similar events occurring early in life awakened my interest in atmospheric optics.

14

Mock Suns and Moons, Light Pillars, and Crosses

On September 15, 1851, five suns were seen in the sky. The simple country people near Geneva, Switzerland, who observed this extraordinary spectacle, were struck with terror. They firmly believed the sun was multiplying itself to set the earth on fire!

What the people actually saw was the real sun and four colored luminous spots called variously *parhelia, mock suns,* or *sun dogs.* A parhelion (from the Greek meaning "beside the sun") is a halo. Although the term "halo" implies ring shape, it is generally applied to all optical phenomena that are produced by ice crystals suspended in the atmosphere and, as we have seen, by those deposited on the ground. In addition to the 22° and 46° halos, other rings, arcs, and splotches of light are sometimes seen in the sky. As a rule, only a few of these effects are observed simultaneously, but at times they make complex figures. If the halos are colored, they are produced by refraction of light by the crystals. If they are white, they are produced by reflection from the crystal faces.

Mock suns. Two bright spots appear on either side of a jet airliner at Omaha's Eppley Airfield. The central spot of illumination is the sun. Taken on January 12, 1963.

Because of the innumerable combinations of crystal types, crystal orientation, crystal motion, and solar elevation angle, a large variety of halos are theoretically possible and many have been seen. The parhelia already mentioned are two unusually bright spots that appear at a distance of about 22° on either side of the sun and at the same elevation. They are especially prominent as the sun approaches the horizon, often showing color, red nearest the sun and blue farthest away. They can be seen about two dozen times a year in the United States and Canada. Similar phenomena occur at a distance of about 46°, but they are seldom seen and much less intense. The corresponding images produced by the moon are called *paraselenae* and also *mock moons.*

Sometimes a faint white circle of light is observed passing through the sun and running parallel to the horizon. The circle goes clear around the heavens and passes through the parhelia, which are often visible at the same time. That is why it is called the *parhelic circle*.

The *subsun* is a reflected image of the sun that appears as far below the horizon as the sun is above the apparent junction of earth and sky. This remarkable phenomenon can therefore only be seen from an airplane or a balloon or a high mountain and is quite rare.

Subsun seen from a balloon. This rare phenomenon was observed over France by two aeronauts, Barral and Bixio, on July 27, 1850. The second sun looked like the reflection of the first from a sheet of water.

During cold weather, when the sun is low in the heavens, a streak of light, white or slightly reddened, is frequently seen extending above and below the sun. When the sun is on the horizon, the luminous streak is glimpsed merely rising above the sun. This *sun* or *light pillar* may extend to about 20° above the luminary and generally ends in a point. The moon also produces this effect. So do artificial lights on earth; at times a forest of glowing vertical shafts is seen.

When a light pillar and a parhelic circle occur at the same time, we see a *sun cross*, bands of white light that intersect over the sun at right angles. This is an impressive phenomenon, and a great deal has been made of it by superstitious people. Crosses are also produced by the moon, as well as by streetlamps, proving the presence of a floating mist of ice crystals in the air.

The *circumzenithal arc* is startlingly beautiful and fleeting. This bright arc, which lasts only a few minutes, gets its name from having its center at the *zenith*, the point of the heavens that is directly overhead. Parallel to the horizon, the arc is about one-fourth of a complete circle and seen some 46° above the sun. Some people mistake it for a rainbow. It is brilliantly colored, red toward the sun and blue to violet on the inside. The effect occurs most often when the sun is about 20° above the horizon and at times when the parhelia of 22° are prominent.

There are a number of other phenomena associated with halos, but they have been seen and measured so rarely that the theories accounting for them are still in some degree questionable. Moreover, many phenomena possible in theory seem so far to have escaped observation. In the United States, halos in some form or other can be seen on the average of about one day in three.

15

Coronas, Iridescent Clouds, and Bishop's Ring

At times a thin veil of clouds covers the moon. Without realizing it, my eye is attracted to this illuminated part of the night sky, and I see a colored ring around and rather close to the moon. This is not a halo, for the ring is smaller and has the reverse order of colors, blue nearest the moon and red farthest away. It is a *corona*.

The simplest form of the corona is the *aureole*, which is seen most frequently. This is a luminous patch of light immediately around the sun or moon. It is bluish white over the inner area and brownish red in the outer portion.

The corona phenomenon becomes really remarkable only when the aureole is surrounded by more beautifully colored rings. As many as three of these rainbow-colored rings have been observed outside the aureole, with the sun or moon at the center —a fourfold corona. Because of its brightness, coronas around the sun are usually the finest of all. They are not noticed as often as coronas around the moon, however, because people naturally avoid looking at the sun. If you look for this at-

Corona formed around the moon. The aureole is plainly visible, with one ring.

mospheric effect, wear dark glasses or make sure that the sun is hidden by the edge of a roof. Sir Isaac Newton (1642-1727), the English scientific genius, observed the solar corona by viewing its reflection in still water.

The corona is due to *diffraction* of sunlight or moonlight by a large number of tiny drops of water in the clouds. Diffraction is the spreading of light waves around obstacles. When a ray of light falls on the edge of an object, it does not continue in a straight line but is turned aside so that it spreads into the shadow region of the object. The various wavelengths forming the white light are diffracted somewhat differently from each other. This causes the separation of white light into the colors of which it is composed.

The radius of the corona is determined by the size of the water droplets. The larger the corona, the smaller the droplets. When the corona consists of more than one ring, it tells us that droplets of different distinct sizes are present in the clouds. When the cloud droplets are of various sizes and none is particularly dominant, they produce only the aureole. In any case, coronas are usually not more than a few degrees in radius. The angular diameter of the sun and of the moon, you will recall, is about a half degree.

On a winter night, when I walk past a well-lit restaurant, I sometimes notice that the table lamps are surrounded by colored rings. The rings are caused by the moisture on the window. They are larger on some parts of the window than on others. Frequently, I see only the aureole, but sometimes the rings are surprisingly beautiful. They are due to the tiny drops of water on the panes of glass, and the more equal the drops are in size, the more lovely they are. These coronas bear a strong resemblance to solar and lunar coronas, but, after all, they are produced in a similar way. In one case, the diffracting drops are on the window, in the other they are in a cloud high up in the atmosphere.

When the droplets are extraordinarily small, as they must become in slowly evaporating thin clouds, the clouds may develop many iridescent borders and patches of irregular shape at distances from the sun up to 30° or more. At the sight of such lovely clouds, people often feel great delight, which is due in large part to the purity of the colors, especially red and green, their delicate mingling, and their bright light. I am spellbound by these *iridescent clouds*, which are presumably only fragments of unusually large and exceptionally brilliant coronas. On one occasion, iridescence was observed on the artificial clouds produced by an airplane writing advertisements in the sky!

Coronas are also the result of diffraction produced by dust particles, though these are rarely seen. After the eruption of the island volcano Krakatau in 1883, a broad reddish-brown ring was often observed around the sun. It had a radius of about 20°. This is known as *Bishop's ring*, named after the Reverend S. E. Bishop of Honolulu who first described it. Similar coronas were seen around the sun after the eruption of two other volcanoes, Mount Pelée in 1902 and Mount Katmai in 1912.

16

Glory, Bouguer's Halo, and Brocken Specter

If an observer happens to be on top of a mountain when the sun is low in the sky, he can sometimes see his own shadow cast on a fog bank or cloud below him. The head of the shadow will be surrounded by rings of light having the same vivid colors, red outermost, as those shown by coronas around the sun and moon. As many as five rings have been seen. The effect is also observed from an airplane flying in sunlight above a cloud layer; the airplane's shadow is encircled by rainbow-like bands. In the nineteenth century, when balloon ascents were prevalent, passengers saw these bands encircling the shadow of the basket of the balloon.

The *glory*, as this phenomenon is called, is a diffraction effect very similar to the corona, appearing at a point directly opposite the sun or moon from the observer. For this reason, it is also called the *anticorona*. When flying toward the sun through a cloud, an aviator frequently sees a corona in front of him and simultaneously a glory behind him.

It is not completely clear whether this phenomenon is pro-

Ulloa's ring. At daybreak one morning on the summit of Pambamarca, in Peru, Antonio de Ulloa observed the head of his shadow in the center of three rainbow-like bands, which were surrounded at a certain distance by a fourth white circular bow.

duced by internal reflection in the droplets of the cloud or fog bank followed by the then forward diffraction of the reflected waves, or whether it is simply a backward diffraction, the droplets diffracting the light in the same direction as that from which it came.

The glory is often surrounded by a fogbow. It has a radius of about 39° and seems farther away than the glory—undoubtedly a psychological effect. This faint, white circular arc or complete ring is called *Bouguer's halo* after Pierre Bouguer, a French mathematician, and also *Ulloa's ring*, after Antonio de Ulloa, a Spanish scientist, both of whom observed and wrote descriptions of the phenomenon in the eighteenth century.

The shadow seen from the mountain may take on the deceptive appearance of a gigantic figure called the *Brocken specter*. Often the figure is encircled by rings of colored light called the *Brocken bow*. This striking spectacle is the same as the glory. It gets its name from the Brocken, the highest peak of the Harz Mountains in Germany, where the "specter" has frequently been observed.

The Brocken specter seems to be a supernatural intervention, and the name it was given still bears witness to the terror it once inspired. The phenomenon gave rise to a legend of a guardian demon supposed to stalk among the solitary mountain ranges in the shape of a wild man of huge stature. He was crowned and girdled with oak leaves and carried a pine tree torn up by the roots. This woodland goblin, who, according to the miners and foresters of the region, strode from glen to glen, even found his place on many of the coins and medals struck out of the silver of the Harz Mountains.

The Brocken specter has, of course, made his appearance in many other parts of the world. An old friend observed the phenomenon as a young man, in about 1920. It was late summer in England, and he was with a party on foot near Mountsorrel, a town situated on the left bank of the Soar River. It was in the granite hills overlooking the river that the specter appeared. Toward sunset, as they were approaching a summit, the boys came upon a gigantic man on horseback. The apparition naturally terrified them, till it faded away. Somewhere in those magic hills there was a real horse and rider, but the boys never encountered them.

Brocken specter. In the summer of 1862, at sunrise, the French artist Stroobant witnessed and sketched the specter. He was in the company of a guide on the plateau upon the summit of the Brocken at the time.

As a child I saw my own shadow cast on the fog simply by standing in front of an open window one night, with a bright light behind me. The shadow of my body was much enlarged, and a glow of light surrounded my head. When I saw this effect, I was filled with wonder. Although I was told it was only my own shadow, I felt it was not so. There was something strange here that challenged that explanation. Now I know it was nothing less than the Brocken specter!

I saw the phenomenon again some years later when I was on a bicycle trip to Bear Mountain Park in New York. The journey took longer than I expected, and it was dark and foggy when I reached the Bear Mountain Bridge that crosses the Hudson. It was here that I encountered the demon. As I was bicycling across the bridge, the glaring headlights of a car shone on me from behind, and I saw my shadow on the fog magnified to a huge size.

Thus, the Brocken specter, which is so spectacular when observed at sunrise or sunset from the summit of a mountain, can be seen occasionally under other conditions. The great size of the phenomenon has been explained in several ways, for example, as the result of the shadow not lying in one plane but extending over a depth of many yards. It is now believed to be an illusion that occurs when you judge your nearby shadow to be at the same distance as objects on the earth seen through the thin underlying cloud.

17
Heiligenschein

In the early morning, when the sun is still low and casts long shadows on the dew-covered grass, a sort of glory can be seen close around the shadow of your own head. This ring of white light is called the *heiligenschein*, which means "halo" in German, and is due to the external reflection of sunlight by the dewdrops.

You can be certain of this effect by looking over the whole lawn and noting how the light increases near the shadow of your head. If you take a few steps, you will see that the glow follows you. If you compare your shadow with that of other people, you will find that the luminous ring surrounds only your own head.

When it was observed in the sixteenth century by Benvenuto Cellini, the famous Italian artist, he thought that the crown of light was a sign of divine favor! He first clearly described the phenomenon, which is sometimes called *Cellini's halo*. However, to any given observer, the dewdrops on the blades of grass rapidly increase in brightness as the shadow of his own head is approached. This is because the light reflected from the outer

Heiligenschein on a meadow covered with dew

surface of a dewdrop is brightest back along the *line of incidence*—the line in the direction of which a surface is struck by a ray of light. The light falls off rapidly as its deviation from that line increases.

If you are ever fortunate enough to take a flight in a balloon, you should watch the shadow of the basket passing over the country beneath you. On fields and meadows covered with dew, it is surrounded by a decided luminous area. This is an especially beautiful form of heiligenschein, which can also be seen round the shadow of an airplane.

Diffraction may play a role in this phenomenon, but it is unknown to what extent. There is a complete lack of experimental material serving as a basis for discussion and inference or intensity measurements. In the field of atmospheric optics there are many imperfectly understood phenomena which deserve further study. Who will solve these mysteries?

18
Luminous Trees

Imagine it is night. In the distance, you hear a car coming toward you through the darkness. Its headlights cast a glare on the road, and someone riding a bicycle happens to cross in front of the bright light so that for a moment you stand in his shadow. Suddenly, the cyclist's dark shape is outlined by a strangely beautiful light apparently radiating from its edge. This is another example of diffraction, in which the beams from the headlights are deflected and penetrate the region of the cyclist's shadow.

A similar phenomenon on a larger scale—*luminous trees*—can be seen in country having mountains. In this case, imagine yourself standing in the shade at the foot of a hill, which is located between yourself and the place where the sun is rising. The upper edge of the mountain is covered with forest and detached trees and shrubs, which are projected as dark objects on a bright, clear sky, except at the exact place where the sun is going to rise. There the trees and shrubs are brilliant white. They appear extremely luminous, even though they are pro-

Luminous trees

jected on a very bright sky, as that part of it surrounding the sun always is. Leaves, twigs, and all the smallest details are delicately preserved. The individual trees and forest seem to be made of pure silver with the skill of the most expert craftsman, and birds flying in this particular spot look like brilliant, white sparks or stars.

Now that you are familiar with this beautiful feature of diffraction—showing how the sun's rays are spread around distant trees and produce, where shadow might be expected, a forest of light—you will more easily observe it when you are in mountainous country.

19
Blue Sky and Sky Brightness

Many people have tried to explain the blue color of the sky, including the Florentine, Leonardo da Vinci, who painted the *Mona Lisa*, famous for its subtle smile, in the sixteenth century. This man of genius was a scientist, as well as a painter, sculptor, architect, and engineer, and he suggested that the blue is the result of a mixture of more or less white light reflected by the atmosphere with the black of space. The idea is obviously wrong, for gray alone could be produced by such a mixture.

It was not until the nineteenth century that a satisfactory explanation was given. The blue sky is a phenomenon due to the selective *scattering* of sunlight by small particles of dust and by molecules of gas. Light traveling in a straight path through the atmosphere is disturbed by these small particles. The effect of this disturbance is to cause the light striking the particles to be diffused and spread out. It is more pronounced for the shorter wavelengths—blue light. Therefore, most of the scattered light is blue, and the sky appears blue. This effect is somewhat similar to diffraction, which is caused by particles with

Daytime on the moon. Astronaut Edwin E. Aldrin, Jr., lunar module pilot, is photographed walking on the moon during the Apollo 11 mission. Note the black sky and the intense contrasts of light. The picture was taken by astronaut Neil A. Armstrong.

diameters of the same order of size, or larger than, the wavelength of the light. Scattering is caused by smaller objects.

The scattering of light by the molecules of air and suspended dust particles gives all parts of the sky a brightness that would otherwise not exist, except that occupied by the sun. This in turn increases the brightness of objects on the earth. If it were not for the brightness of the sky, shadows from the sun's light would be very dark. When the sun shines upon a tree in an open field, for example, most of the light entering the shadow comes from the sky. On a bright day, the amount of illumination in such a shadow is extremely high.

Without the diffusion of sunlight by the air, the sky would be black in the daytime! The stars would be visible, together with the sun, which would shine forth brilliantly from the surrounding blackness. There would be great contrasts of light, harsh shadows and dazzling bright areas. Our astronauts observed such conditions when they walked on the airless moon.

20
Colors and Duration of Twilight

During clear weather, as the sun rises and sets, a number of dramatic changes occur over large parts of the sky, particularly the eastern and western. The striking, often brilliant, colors seen at these times are produced by the same process that causes the blue color of the sky—scattering.

As mentioned earlier, the thickness of the atmosphere that light must pass through increases noticeably with decrease of the sun's elevation. Due to the additional amount of intervening dust and air particles, the scattering of the sun's light may be so pronounced that only the longer waves toward the red end of the spectrum succeed in getting through. Then the sky shows its beautiful rosy colors.

Daylight is not followed abruptly by darkness after sunset because the air overhead is still in sunlight and scatters it down to us. Night comes on slowly, as the sun sinks farther below the horizon. The interval of incomplete darkness following sunset is called *twilight*.

Civil twilight lasts until the sun's center is 6° below the hori-

zon, when the light has become too dim for outdoor activities. However, it is still twenty times brighter than the light of the full moon. *Astronomical twilight* ends when the sun's center is 18° below the horizon, when the sky is so dark that the faintest stars can be seen. The same phenomena recur in reverse order before sunrise.

The time it takes the sun to move 18° toward or away from the horizon depends upon the path of the sun and, therefore, in ordinary latitudes, it depends upon the season of the year. When the path is very oblique to the horizon, as in the summer, the duration of the twilight period will be longer than when the path is more perpendicular. The duration of this interval also varies with the latitude, and this variation is greater still. Twi-

Sun that never sets. Taken at Japan's Showa Base in Antarctica in midsummer of 1972, this time exposure shows how the sun moves parallel to the horizon at the poles. The camera's shutter was opened at 20-minute intervals to record the movement of the sun from right to left.

light is shortest at the equator (about 1¼ hours) because the sun's daily path is there perpendicular to the horizon. In *The Rime of the Ancient Mariner*, Samuel Taylor Coleridge, the English poet, refers to this when the ship reaches the equator:

> The sun's rim dips, the stars rush out:
> At one stride comes the dark . . .

In the latitude of the United States, the average length of twilight exceeds 1½ hours. Its duration is greatest in midsummer, when it is more than two hours. And at the poles of the earth, where the sun's daily path is parallel to the horizon, twilight is about 2½ months in duration!

The *purple light* is one of the most interesting of all twilight phenomena. When the sun is 4° to 5° below the horizon, the strongest development of the purple light can be seen in the west. Buildings facing this direction are flooded with a purple glow. The soil and the trunks of trees have a warm tint. In the center of the city, in narrow streets from where the western horizon cannot be viewed, the general illumination of the buildings tells us that the purple light is shining. The various brilliant colors of twilight are also produced by scattering. The purple light is the joint effect of red-rich light scattered down from a dusty layer in the middle atmosphere and blue-rich light scattered by molecules still farther up in the atmosphere.

The intensity of the phenomenon varies a great deal from day to day. If you ever see the deep purple fall over a great city, as I did one evening in New York, you will never forget it. The weather had cleared up after a series of rainy days, and the development of the purple light was strikingly beautiful. Out walking with a friend, I was brought to an abrupt stop by the sight of the buildings along Central Park South bathed in violet light. The effect was to turn New York into an unreal city, which looked like the backdrop for a play. The tall buildings appeared to be cut from colored cardboard. Silently I waited, expecting some colossal actor to appear on the stage. But the light finally faded. Darkness fell, and the drama was over.

The rainbow that appears after a raging storm arouses in some feelings of cheerfulness and joy. The colors of twilight, on the other hand, give one the sense of great calm. This is due to the broad bands of interflowing color, lying so flat across the heavens at twilight as to be almost horizontal. Wherever it is to be found in the landscape, the horizontal line is known to produce a feeling of serenity.

21

Sun Drawing Water, Crepuscular Rays, and Noah's Ark

Most of us have observed the lovely phenomenon of the *sun drawing water*. Often in the late afternoon and sometimes in the early morning, beams of light from the sun can be seen shining through rifts in the clouds. Some of these beams become stronger or weaker or move from one place to another, depending on the shifting of the clouds. Now and then the entire landscape is filled with them. The beams look like they are due to the sun evaporating water from a distant river or lake. But this popular idea is incorrect.

The beams are merely rays of the sun. Finding their way through openings in the clouds, they are made luminous by the dust in their paths that scatters the light. The beam of a bright searchlight at night or the projection beam in a movie theater are similar effects. In each case, there is a contrast between the myriads of illuminated dust particles and the darker portions of the surrounding air. Many people believe that the "sun drawing water" is a good weather sign. Some say it tells us rain is coming, others that it will continue fair. However, it obviously has no significance either way.

Sailors once called the phenomenon the "backstays of the sun." In nautical language, a backstay is a rope or stay extending from a masthead to the side of a ship, and slanting a little aft, to assist in supporting the mast. The natives of Polynesia, islands of the central Pacific Ocean, call it the "ropes of Maui." Maui is the chief culture hero of the Polynesian race. It is said he took the hair of Hina, his sister or wife, or some green flax, and made a noose or net with which he snared the sun. Then with a club he had gotten from his grandmother, he beat the sun until it agreed to move more slowly. And in parts of England the spectacle is referred to as "Jacob's ladder." This is the ladder described in Genesis, reaching from heaven to earth, on which Jacob saw in a dream angels ascending and descending.

The sun drawing water is a phenomenon very similar to *crepuscular rays*—alternating lighter and darker bands, rays and shadows, which appear to spread apart in fanlike order from the region of the sun at about twilight. Literally, this term means "twilight rays," and it is applied to two quite different phenomena. It refers to shadows cast across the purple light by cloud tops that are high enough and far enough away from the observer to interrupt the progress of some of the sunlight that would ordinarily produce the purple light. And it refers to shadows and rays made visible by dust in the lower atmosphere. Towering clouds also cause this effect, which is a more frequent occurrence. But the clouds may be rather close to the observer and the sun need not be below the horizon.

Whether their common origin, the sun, is above or below the horizon, all such crepuscular rays seem first to diverge. At times they are visible clear across the sky. These rays also appear to

Crepuscular rays. Beams of light, finding their way through rifts in a cumulus cloud, seem to radiate from the sun like spokes from the hub of a great wheel.

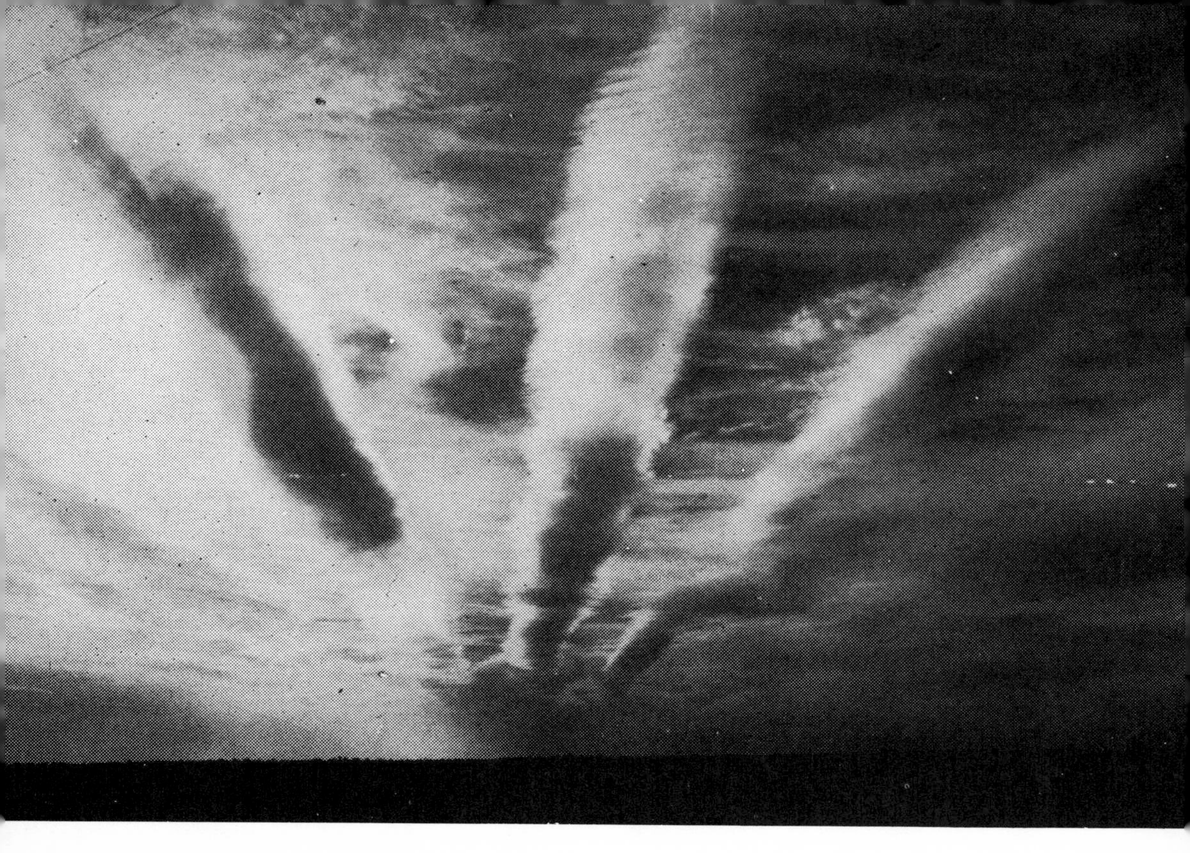

Noah's ark. Taken at Lakehurst, New Jersey, December 1, 1927.

bend into the shape of an arch on the way and finally move toward the point on the celestial sphere which lies opposite the sun from the observer, where they are known as *anticrepuscular rays*.

Here the facts are not what they seem, for the rays are practically parallel, since they all come from the sun some 93,000,000 miles away. The apparent divergence, arching, and convergence are illusions due to *perspective*—the appearance to the eye of objects in respect to their relative distance and positions. A straight stretch of railway gives the same illusion. The rails providing the runway for the train seem to have little breadth a mile away in either direction, but they are extended in width where the observer stands.

Beams of light can also originate from the moon, but they are very weak. They can only be seen when the scattering of light by the dust particles is strong. This rare phenomenon causes in many the feeling of ominous gloom.

Another interesting perspective effect is *Noah's ark*. This is a series of straight, parallel, narrow bands of cloud that appear to spring from common points on opposite sides of the horizon and to separate to their widest spread as they approach the point of the heavens directly above the observer. Here again the approach of railroad tracks toward each other, as the eye looks down the tracks, is a good analogy. The phenomenon looks like a colossal vessel in the sky, narrow at both ends and wide in the middle. It obviously gets its name from the ark in which, according to the Bible, Noah and his family were saved at the time of the Deluge.

22
Moon Illusion

Have you ever thought why the full moon looks bigger when it is close to the horizon than when it is high up in the heavens? The change between the apparent sizes of the full moon, or of the sun, on rising or setting and at its highest point in the sky is a familiar sight. The rising moon can look very large, but when it is well up in the heavens it looks quite small, and the huge tomato-red setting sun is an extraordinary sight. Even the constellations look larger when near the horizon, in that the apparent distance between individual stars is greater.

This phenomenon has puzzled many people, and various explanations have been given for it. The optical illusion has been attributed to the fact that the fully risen moon cannot be easily compared to objects on the earth, as it can at the horizon. If the moon is observed next to a distant house, for example, and if its image is about the same size as the house, then it appears as large as a house. Since the house is quite large, the moon must be large. This explanation is incorrect because the illusion occurs over desert or water, where there are no familiar

Sun illusion. The rising sun is seen from the Vatican Observatory, Castel Gandolfo. The medieval castle on the summit of the mountain is at Rocca Priora, 6½ miles away. Photographed on color film with a reflecting telescope by C. Treusch, S.J., in collaboration with D. J. K. O'Connell.

terrestrial objects for comparison.

Some people have said that color produces a difference in apparent size. Because of the selective scattering by the atmosphere of the shorter wavelengths of light, the horizon moon is often much redder than the moon when it is overhead. Others have attributed the illusion to the dimness of the full horizon moon in the twilight sky compared with the brighter zenith moon in the dark night sky. Still others have said it is the result of the change in the elevation of the observer's eyes. None of these theories is supported by recent experimental evidence, however.

There now seems to be little doubt that this is a phenomenon of perspective. To most people, the sky looks like a great dome, low and flattish, whose circular rim rests on the horizon. The moon appears to move on the inner surface of this dome, which appears to be farther away near the horizon than overhead. But the actual distance of the moon, and its actual angular diameter, remains the same throughout the moon's course from rising to setting. Consequently, in order to make up for its seemingly greater distance when on the horizon, the size of the moon increases. The size increase of the sun and moon is therefore a false perception. Lately, scientists have demonstrated that the horizon moon looks larger because it is seen over terrain, which gives the effect of greater distance—a theory proposed by the Greco-Egyptian astronomer, geographer, and geometer Claudius Ptolemy eighteen hundred years ago. They believe this may play the major role in one of the most remarkable illusions in nature.

Conclusion

We have considered the optical phenomena associated with the interaction of light with atmospheric gases, dust particles, ice crystals, and water drops. In general, the effects are due to refraction, reflection, diffraction, and scattering. Some optical effects are also due to perspective. The features caused by refraction are more numerous than those produced in other ways.

The phenomena described are truly wonderful, and the fanciful names given to them—Brocken specter, Fata Morgana, Noah's ark—reflect their awesome and beautiful nature. Indeed, some of these spectacles are so weird that they seem to belong to an order of existence beyond nature, and they help to perpetuate man's belief in the supernatural.

In addition to the effects observed in light from extraterrestrial sources, phenomena can be seen in light from sources within the atmosphere—such as scintillation of city lights, coronas around table lamps, and crosses intersecting streetlights. And some

MACY'S
to be thrifty

phenomena, like halos and rainbows, are seen on the ground as well as in the sky.

As mentioned at the beginning of this book, chance favors the prepared mind. Having been acquainted with the circumstances, you will from this time on have a greater chance of seeing these optical effects. There are many other effects not described or briefly mentioned here, such as shadows cast by the sun. Once your interest is awakened, you may want to study them. Moreover, there are optical effects that are not completely understood, providing research opportunities for young scientists. Even the rainbow is capable of further investigation. Reasonably good explanations may be formulated for the principal rainbows in terms of *geometric optics*, refractions and reflections at the water-drop surfaces. But a complete theory of the rainbow can be built up only in terms of diffraction effects. This theory permits the computation of fogbows, rainbows, and supernumerary rainbows all in a single scheme.

The best place to view most of these atmospheric displays is on the open sea. There, there is an unobstructed horizon, allowing for observation of the whole sky at one time, and no artificial illumination of the sky to interfere with the displays occurring at night. The mountains and the desert also afford excellent opportunities to observe optical phenomema. However, these wonders can be seen by city and country dwellers, too. A surprising number of observations of light and color in the open air are possible no matter where you live.

Shadow of a skyscraper. A bright sun shining on the Empire State Building casts an unusual shadow on low-hanging clouds blanketing New York City. Observers on top of the skyscraper were provided with this rare sight on January 1, 1939.

Acknowledgments

Grateful acknowledgment is made to the following institutions that have given permission for the use of illustrations:

National Aeronautics and Space Administration, Washington, D.C., page 87

National Oceanic and Atmospheric Administration, Rockville, Maryland, endpaper and pages 18, 57

The New York Public Library, Picture Collection, New York, N.Y., pages 41, 42, 43, 52

Specola Vaticana, Stato dello Citta del Vaticano, pages 25, 99

Wide World Photos, New York, N.Y., pages 28, 33, 68, 90–91, 95, 102

Yerkes Observatory, Williams Bay, Wisconsin, pages 21, 31

The pictures on pages 47, 49, 65, 69, 72, 76, and 78 are from *L'Atmosphere, Description Des Grandes Phénomenes De La Nature*, by Camille Flammarion, Deuxième Édition, Librairie Hachette Et Cie, Paris, 1873. The picture on page 84 is from *The Aerial World* by G. Hartwig, Longmans, Green, and Co., London, 1877. The picture on page 46 is from "Photographische Aufnahmen einer mehrfachen Luftspieglung" by Wilhelm Hillers, plate XXVIII, *Physikalische Zeitschrift*, vol. XIV, Verlag von S. Hirzel, Leipzig, 1913. The frontispiece is from *Meteorologische Optik* by J. M. Pernter, vol. III, Wilhelm Braumüller, Wien und Leipzig, 1906. The picture on pages 36–37 is from "Description of some remarkable Atmospheric Reflections and Refractions, observed in the Greenland Sea" by William Scoresby, Jr., plate XVIII, *Transactions of the Royal Society of Edinburgh*, vol. IX, Royal Society of Edinburgh, Edinburgh, 1823. The picture on page 61 is from "Double Rainbow" by P. G. Tait, *Nature*, vol. X, Macmillan and Co., London and New York, 1874.

Annotated Bibliography

The following is a list of basic sources of information on atmospheric optics used in the preparation of this book. The sources present historical summaries, and their contents are based largely on surveys of literature in the field. In addition to these books, other sources were used for specific phenomena. On UFOs two main works were consulted: *Final Report of the Scientific Study of Unidentified Flying Objects Conducted by the University of Colorado*, Edward U. Condon, Scientific Director (New York: E. P. Dutton, published with Colorado Associated University Press, 1969); and *Aliens in the Skies: the Scientific Rebuttal to the Condon Committee Report*, United States House Committee on Science and Astronautics (New York: Putnam, 1969). Chiefly, *Glossary of Meteorology*, edited by Ralph E. Huschke (Boston: American Meteorological Society, second printing with corrections, 1970) was accepted as authority for terms and definitions.

Humphreys, W. J. *Physics of the Air.* 3rd. ed. revised. New York and London: McGraw-Hill Book Company, Inc., 1940.

An orderly assemblage of the facts and theories of the exceedingly numerous and important physical phenomena of the earth's atmosphere.

Malone, Thomas F. (ed.) *Compendium of Meteorology.* Boston: American Meteorological Society, 1951.

A survey of the current state of meteorology. One-hundred-eight articles by 102 authors comprise the book, which is divided into 25 sections.

Minnaert, M. *Light and Colour in the Open Air.* Translated by H. M. Kremer-Priest and revised by K. E. Brian Jay. London: G. Bell & Sons Ltd., 1940.

The main points of some thousands of articles on optical phenomena from every possible periodical.

Pernter, J. M., and Exner, F. M. *Meteorologische Optik.* 4 vols. Wien und Leipzig: Wilhelm Braumüller, 1902–1910.

A major German reference work on meteorological optics issued in four parts. Begun by J. M. Pernter and at his death, in 1908, completed by F. M. Exner.

Index